Cats

LORNA SCOBIE

SCHOLASTIC

I am a collector.

Today, I'm going to collect cats.

I *love* cats.

At the moment, I have no cats.

But I do have a plan.

I don't like mice . . .

. . . but mice like cheese.

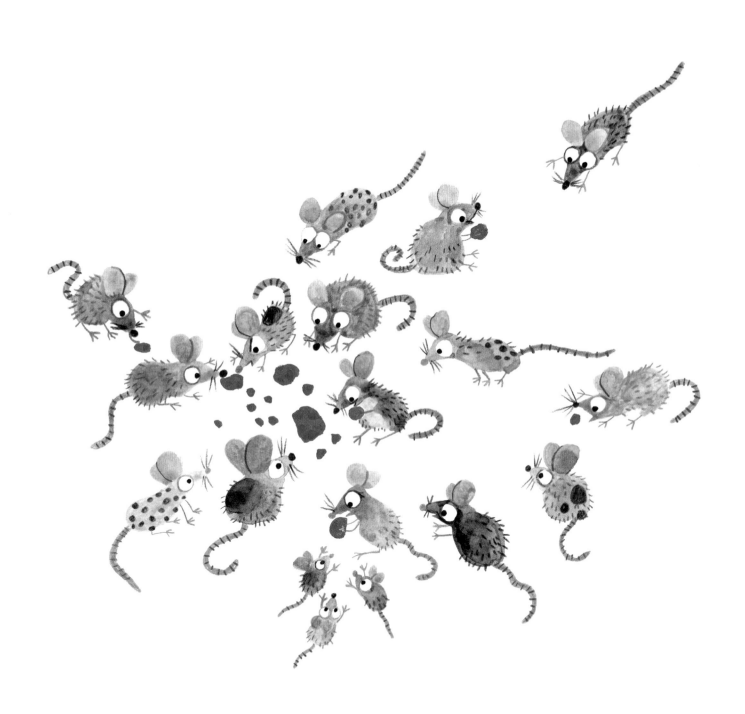

And CATS like mice.

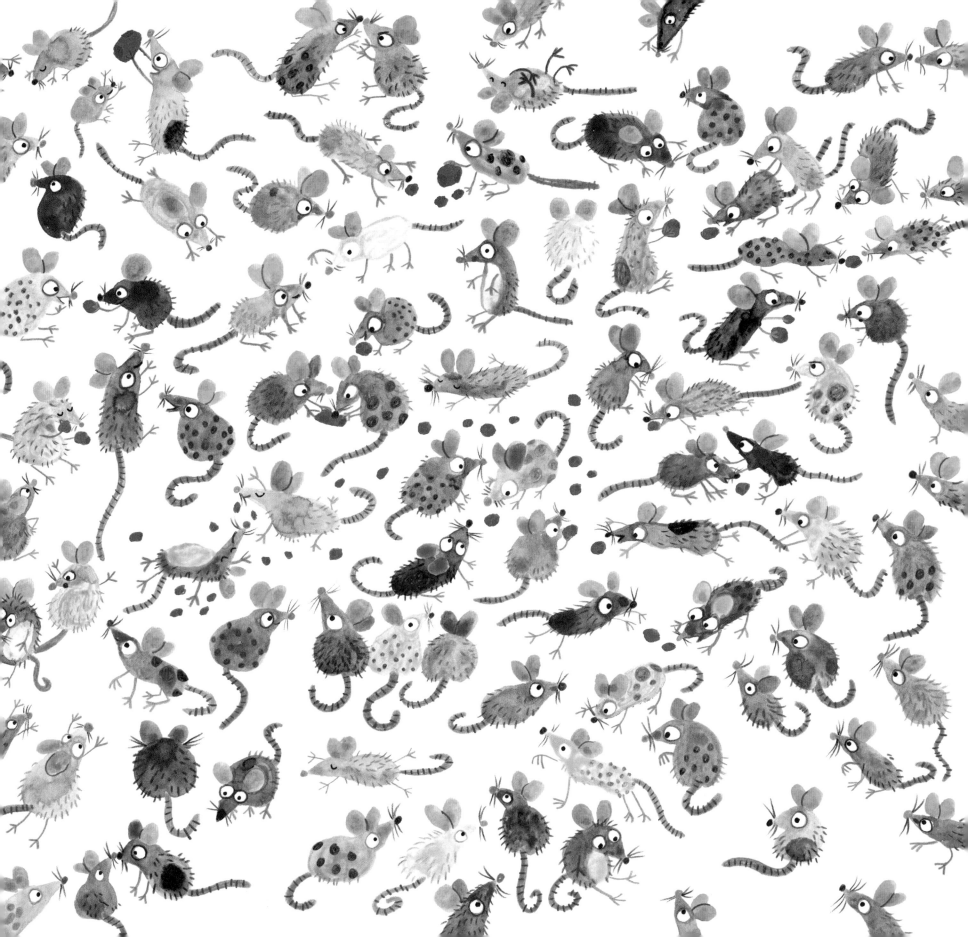

I now have
some cats.

I am a collector of cats!

At the moment, I have only twelve cats.

Two fluffy cats,

three spotty
cats,

four fat cats

and three
thin cats.

This is not enough.
Not to worry, I have a plan.

I still have some cheese.
And mice like cheese,
and cats like mice.

I have now collected so many cats!

I can't even count them.

Fluffy cats.

Spotty cats.

Fat cats.

Thin cats.

Big, stripy cats?

I DO love all cats.
But I'm not sure
about these big ones.

Perhaps being a collector
of cats isn't for me.

I have a plan . . .

I love cheese.

I'm going to collect cheese instead.